BUMPER BOOK
1995

FRED BASSET

by ALEX GRAHAM

Orion Books Ltd
Orion House
5 Upper St Martin's Lane
London WC2H 9EA

First published by Orion 1995

Drawings by Michael Martin

© Associated Newspapers plc 1995

ISBN 0 752 80291 7

Printed and bound in Italy

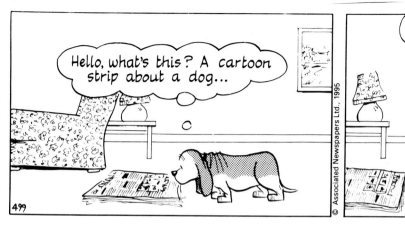

27/1

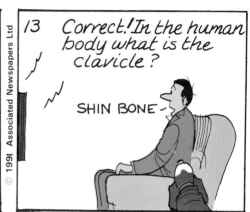

I'M TIRED AND MY FEET ARE KILLING ME.

.. I'VE HAD A LOUSY DAY AT THE OFFICE ...

.. I THINK I'M GETTING A COLD AND I RECKON IT'S GOING TO RAIN.

.. MY HEADACHE'S GETTING WORSE ...

ALL I WANT TO DO IS SIT DOWN QUIETLY AND READ A BOOK ...

.. BUT AS A DOG OWNER I MUST ENSURE THAT MY PET GETS HIS DAILY EXERCISE.

I'm lucky to be owned by such a wonderful human being.

10/2

ALEX GRAHAM

FRED!

DINNER, FRED!

Coming!

11-7

Mm.! A tin of Doggydins.

I must say it always looks more enticing in the television advertisements.

GRAHAM

FRED! HAVE YOU BEEN AT THE CORNFLAKES AGAIN?

YOU HAVE, HAVEN'T YOU?

His powers of observation are really amazing, you know!

602

He's going to give up his job, buy a country mansion with swimming pool, tennis courts and a garage full of posh cars, a villa in the South of France and a yacht to cruise around the Mediterranean

MBM · 603

That's if he wins the Lottery, of course!

OOoer.... What's that?

Whatever it was, I didn't like the way it wiggled!

612 · MBM

She's just cooked a lovely ham — smells delicious...

613

...And now she's popped out to the shops and left me here all alone. But, of course, I wouldn't dream of touching it...

Not until it's cooled down, anyway!

MBM

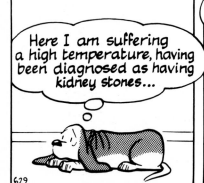

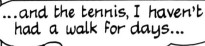

20-6

He's become completely engrossed in building this sand castle...

...but I think this little lad would like his bucket and spade back now!

While they're out there swimming, I'll take a nap on the air bed...

Oops! That's torn it...

... I should've had my nails clipped!